Fun at the Playground
A divertirse en el parque infantil

by Deborah Schecter

ISBN: 978-1-338-70275-0
Illustrated by Anne Kennedy
Copyright © 2020 by Deborah Schecter. All rights reserved.
Published by Scholastic Inc., 557 Broadway, New York, NY 10012

10 9 8 7 6   68   23 24 25 26/0

Printed in Jiaxing, China. First printing, June 2020.

◼ SCHOLASTIC

I go in.

Entro.

I go out.

Salgo.

I go high.

Subo hasta arriba.

I go low.

Bajo hasta abajo.

I go up.

Subo.

I go down.

Bajo.

At the playground,
I get around!

¡En el parque infantil
voy a todos lados!